Contents

Stories written by Geoffrey Cowan
Illustrated by Ray and Christine Mutimer
Strips by Sue Pearson

The picture strips in this book
appeared previously in *Buttons*
comic.

Published in Great Britain by
World International Publishing Ltd,
An Egmont Company, Egmont House, PO Box 111,
Great Ducie Street, Manchester M60 3BL.
Printed in Italy
ISBN 0 7498 0271 5

Slow boat

1   Charlie was woken from his nap one morning by a breathless Captain Mildred. "Charlie, come quickly," she gasped.

2   "Lewis is planning to sail around the world. He says he is setting off today." Charlie did not like the sound of that.

3   "Don't go!" Arnold was crying, when they arrived. "I'll never see you again." But Lewis had made up his mind.

4   He gave a grand speech to all the Merrytwit islanders, standing on an old coconut box. "The time has come . . ."

5   ". . . for me to pack a few things and head for the high seas. I am just an explorer at heart. I need to travel."

6   "Where will you go?" asked Trader. "What will you eat?" said Arnold. "Will you be coming back?" asked Charlie.

7   But Lewis could not answer. The truth of the matter was he had not really thought about it. "Er . . . well," he began.

8   "Do you have a life-jacket?" "Don't forget a torch!" "Where is your map?" His friends threw questions at him.

9   Lewis began to wish he had never decided to sail around the world. It was scary and he would miss his friends.

10   Luckily, Mary the Hover Fairy put her wand, Houdini, to work. "Look!" gasped Lewis, secretly relieved.

11   "My boat has sprung a leak! I will just have to cancel the voyage." "Hip, hip, hooray!" cheered Charlie Chalk.

The Big Top

"And now, presenting for your entertainment, the famous clown, Charlie CHAAALK!" announced the ring-master as he raised his top hat and addressed the eager audience. Charlie came cartwheeling into the ring and everyone cheered. Suddenly, everything began to spin and the roar of the crowd grew louder and louder. Charlie closed his eyes.

When he opened them, he found himself lying in bed, in his caravan on Merrytwit. He sat up and pulled back the curtain. The window was open and Charlie realized it was the roar of the sea that he could hear.

"I've been dreaming!" he thought. "But I do miss my days back in the circus! They were so exciting!"

In fact, Charlie kept thinking about them all that day.

"Good morning, Charlie!" called Lewis, when he saw Charlie strolling along the beach. But Charlie did not even hear him. He didn't see Edward, either, who was sleeping on the sand. Thud! Charlie tripped over him. Later, when Charlie headed back along the track beside the beach, he almost stepped out in front of Trader's taxi. Trader tooted his horn and Charlie jumped clear just in time.

"Whatever's the matter with Charlie?" Trader asked Lewis. In fact, before long, all the Merrytwit folk were so worried about him they went to tell Captain Mildred.

"Here comes Charlie now!" said Mildred. "Let's ask him what's wrong."

So Charlie told them about his dream and how he had been thinking about all the exciting things that used to happen at the circus. "I do like living on Merrytwit and having so many friends," he said. "But if only I could just see the Big Top once more!" He sighed, sadly.

"A, he will and, B, I have an idea!" announced Captain Mildred to the others, as Charlie walked off, deep in thought, towards his caravan.

So while Lewis visited Charlie, and asked to look at all the circus pictures that he kept under the bed, the others happily obeyed Captain Mildred's orders and set to work.

For once, Trader did not want to trade anything in exchange for all the big sheets he brought from his store. Mary the Hover Fairy helped Mildred fetch needles, thread and a set of old sails from the hold of the Buttercup. Arnold called some rabbits and they all went off in search of a straight, thick fallen branch. Everyone was very busy.

All the while, Lewis stayed with Charlie – until it was evening. "I remember the flag on the Big Top!" said Charlie, pointing to an old picture. "Oh, and I remember the circus juggler! His act was very exciting!" Charlie went on until, at last, he fell asleep. Lewis woke him just long enough to see him into bed, and then crept out.

The other Merrytwit folk worked late into the night, under the light of Trader's lamps. But Charlie did not know. He was dreaming of the circus Big Top once more.

When he woke, late the next morning, Charlie peered out of his window again – and could hardly believe his eyes. There, on the beach, was a Big Top! The huge, brightly-coloured tent was held in place by lots of ropes. Charlie rushed down to look at it. As he lifted the entrance flap and hurried in, all the Merrytwit folk were waiting.

"Roll up! Roll up! Introducing Charlie Chalk, the famous clown!" announced Captain Mildred, just like a real ring-master. "Welcome to the Merrytwit Big Top!"

"We built it especially for you, Charlie!" said Arnold, proudly.

"It's . . . magical!" Charlie gasped with delight.

"Well, Houdini, my wand, did give the Big Top its stripes!" smiled Mary.

Charlie hardly knew what to say, except to thank all his friends for their kindness. But, outside, the bright blue sky suddenly turned dark as storm-clouds gathered. A strong wind blew in from the sea and very soon turned into a gale. The circus tent groaned and strained as the wind tugged at its ropes.

"Secure those ropes, everyone!" called Captain Mildred. "Jump to it!" Charlie and the others rushed outside. But no sooner had they all taken a firm hold of them when an extra-strong gust lifted the Big Top clean into the air, carrying the Merrytwit folk with it!

"Let go!" shouted Mildred, as the islanders were carried higher and higher. In no time, they all dropped safely down again. They landed in all sorts of strange places. Lewis fell into a rock pool; Edward landed on top of a palm tree and immediately fell asleep in its big leaves. Charlie landed beside Captain Mildred on the deck of the Buttercup.

"At least no one was hurt!" said Captain Mildred, as the storm passed.

"But I'm afraid the Big Top's been blown clean away, Charlie!" added Lewis. "We're very sorry!"

"Don't be!" laughed Charlie, his cheerful self again. "I've just remembered – that was the most exciting thing that ever happened to the Big Top!"

The show starts with 's'

. . . and so do lots of things in this picture of Charlie putting on a special show for his Merrytwit friends. Try and find at least ten!

Read all about it!

1   Charlie Chalk was busy beachcombing one day, when he spotted a piece of paper. "I wonder who left that there?" he thought.

2   But when he picked it up, Charlie found it was a newsletter. "Hmm! The Merrytwit Bugle," said Charlie, reading.

3   "It says it was written by Trader Jones. I'll ask him all about it," decided Charlie, folding the paper and setting off.

4   "Oh, yes," said Trader. "This is very old. I used to type a news page about once a month, but I'm too busy now."

5   "We only had one copy," he went on. "It was passed around all the islanders. It used to be popular with everyone."

6   "I think I'll write a new one," said Charlie Chalk. "It sounds quite easy." But it took longer than he thought!

7   By the morning, Charlie was very tired. "Here is the new newsletter," he yawned. "But there will be no more."

8   "It is too much work," he went on. Just then, Mary came along. "Leave it to me," she said, hovering off at top speed.

9   Next day, Charlie was surprised to see a banner pulled by a model plane. It told everyone to meet in the clearing.

10   "Where's the newsletter?" Charlie asked, when everyone arrived. "There isn't one!" said Mary, with a wink.

11   "Instead of a newsletter, let's have a weekly meeting. It's easier and more fun!" she said, handing out sandwiches!

Captain Mildred calling!

"Pay attention! A, name the crossword picture-clues and, B, write the words in the correct spaces. Some letters are already written in for you. Good luck! Over and out!"

1 DOWN

2 ACROSS

3 ACROSS

3 DOWN

4 DOWN

5 ACROSS

Keeping cool

"PHEW! It's so hot!" gasped Charlie, as the midday sun beat down on Merrytwit. "My caravan is like an oven – even with the door open!"

Then Charlie had an idea how to make it cooler inside. He pulled the curtains to keep the sun out. "Now I just need a shade for the door!" he muttered, hurrying off. Charlie knew where tall jungle grass grew, and went to cut some. Later, he hung it over his clothes-line to dry out while he visited Trader's store.

"I'll trade you three coconuts for a length of elastic," he told Trader.

"Make it four!" replied Trader.

Charlie agreed, then he went back to his caravan and stretched the elastic across the top of the doorway. Next, Charlie tied the grass to the elastic, so it hung down to the floor.

"A perfect door-shade!" he said. "That will keep the sun out!"

Charlie decided it worked so well that Captain Mildred might like one, as well, to hang up in the cabin doorway of the Buttercup.

He had some spare elastic. So he cut some more grass and soon made another door-shade. Then he set off along the beach.

"Must keep the Buttercup ship-shape!" Captain Mildred said, balancing on some steps, painting the funnel.

"Hello, Captain Mildred!" called Charlie, walking up the gangplank. "I've a surprise for you!"

As he spoke, there was a sudden warm gust which made the grass door-shade rustle and blow towards Mildred.

"A, that was certainly a surprise, Charlie and, B, I haven't a spare skirt to wear while I clean this one!" she frowned, getting up.

"Sorry!" said Charlie. "I only came to bring you this. It's a . . ." Charlie stopped and thought hard. "Er, have you a pair of scissors, please?"

Puzzled, Mildred fetched them. Charlie snipped the grass so it was much shorter. "There," he said, "a grass skirt!"

"Thank you, Charlie!" said Captain Mildred, trying it on. "It's much cooler to work in!"

"And very becoming!" chuckled Charlie. "What better to wear on a tropical island!"

"Oo . . . er!" she cried, startled. Mildred fell off the steps, splashing the skirt of her uniform with paint. Luckily, she was not hurt.

Shadow shapes

On a sunny day, you will see lots of shadows. Look for your own shadow shape! See if you can match the ones here with the objects in the picture. What are they?

The picnic hamper

1   Trader was on his way to pick up Charlie one day, when he spotted a big basket. "I wonder what is in here?" he said.

2   He opened the basket and found it was full of delicious food. "It's a picnic hamper!" Trader cried, feeling hungry.

3   So he took it to his hut and told everyone. "A feast!" said Arnold. "It makes a change from bananas!"

4   "Wait!" said Captain Mildred. "We cannot eat the food because, A, we don't know who it all belongs to . . ."

5   ". . . and, B, they might be looking for it." "Yes," said Charlie, sadly. "The basket must belong to someone."

6　"Exactly," said Captain Mildred. "We will keep it outside Trader's hut. If no one comes for it by tomorrow, we'll have it."

7　Although everyone agreed, they were all hoping no one would collect the food. Arnold even waited by the basket!

8　At lunch-time, Lewis rushed round to Trader's to see if it had been taken. "I can't wait much longer!" he said.

9　Just then, Litterbug came by. He did not look very happy. "What's the matter with you today?" asked Lewis, puzzled.

10　"I've lost my food hamper," said Litterbug. "I was going to share it but now I'm afraid it's back to bananas!"

11　"We've found your hamper!" cried Lewis. And that afternoon, Merrytwit celebrated the news with a huge picnic!

Butterfly beauty

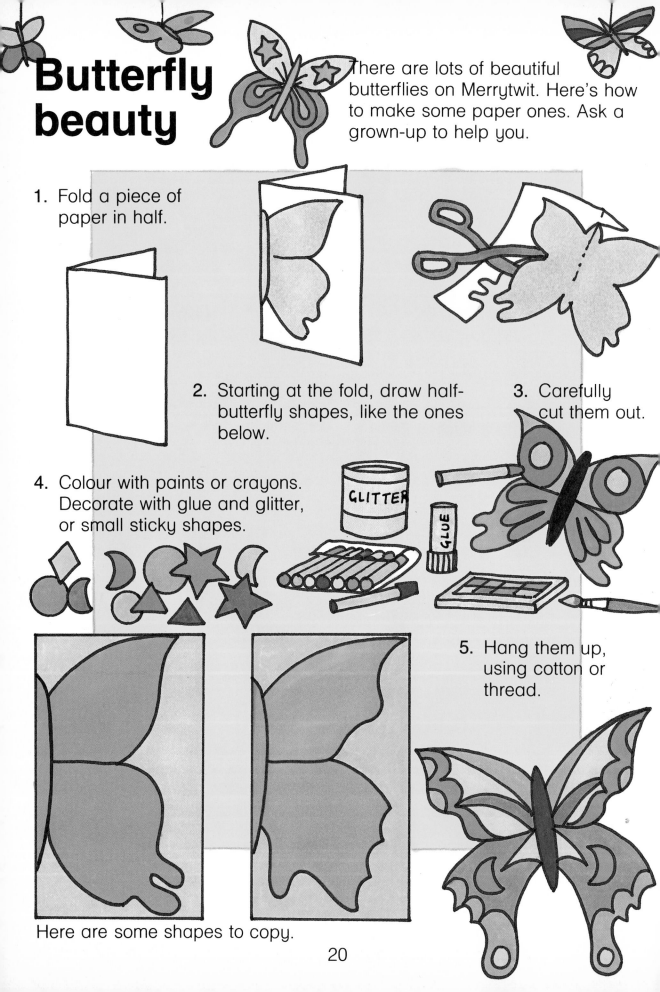

There are lots of beautiful butterflies on Merrytwit. Here's how to make some paper ones. Ask a grown-up to help you.

1. Fold a piece of paper in half.

2. Starting at the fold, draw half-butterfly shapes, like the ones below.

3. Carefully cut them out.

4. Colour with paints or crayons. Decorate with glue and glitter, or small sticky shapes.

GLITTER

GLUE

5. Hang them up, using cotton or thread.

Here are some shapes to copy.

Monkey business

All sorts of creatures live in the jungle. Trace this monkey on to a piece of paper. Colour him, then cut out. Fold in half, down the centre line, stick together and hang him up by his tail – perhaps on a door handle!

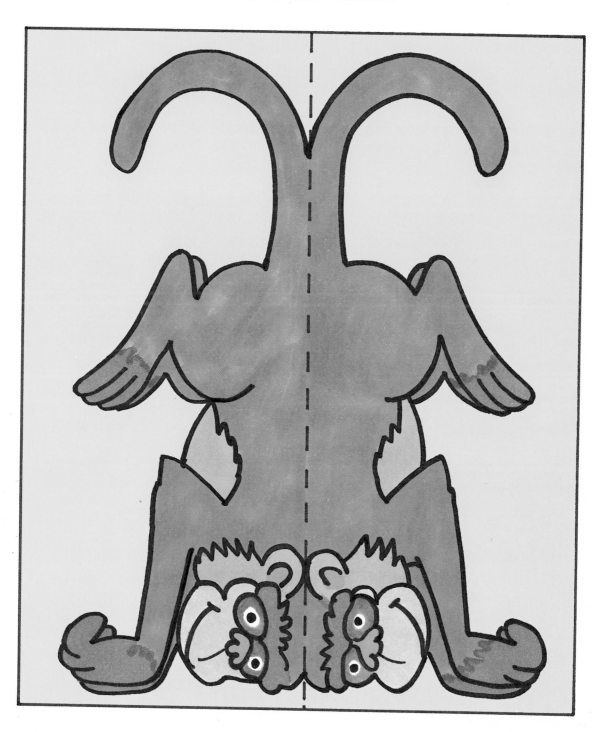

The message

1   Arnold and Lewis had a message. "Captain Mildred told us to come at four o'clock," said Lewis. "We are half an hour late."

2   "Sorry, Lewis. I couldn't help falling into that hole," said Arnold. But Captain Mildred was not waiting anyway.

3   "She must be at Charlie's," said Lewis, as they walked on. But when they reached the caravan, it was empty.

4   "Hello, Trader! Captain Mildred?" cried Arnold, looking in Trader's hut. "They are not here, either. No one is."

5   "Where can they be?" sighed Lewis. "This is very puzzling." Arnold began to cry. "Perhaps they have left us!"

6 "Maybe they all caught a boat and went off without us!" he sniffed. "Oh, don't be so silly, Arnold!" smiled Lewis.

7 "I'll climb up on your shoulders and have a look around," he went on. After a struggle, Lewis managed to get up.

8 "I can't see anyone. Look out! Here comes a coconut!" yelled Lewis. Arnold managed to step out of the way, but. . .

9 . . . he stepped under another one! CLONK! went the coconut on Lewis's head. "Ouch! That hurt!" he said, falling.

10 "Well, I see you have started already," said Mildred, coming from nowhere. "Started what?" asked Arnold.

11 "Collecting the coconuts, of course! It's harvest time again, which is why everyone is here!"

The ready, get set, go game

It's baking hot on Merrytwit. Charlie wants a dip in the cool pool. Arnold wants a fruit drink in the caravan. Play this game with a friend. Decide who will be Charlie and who will be Arnold. Put your counters at either end of the jungle path. Take it in turns to throw a die. Move the same number of squares as dots on the die. If you land on a message, you must do what it says. The winner is the first one to reach the other end. *Ready, get set, GO!*

Shelter from storm – miss a turn

Roly-poly down a hill – throw again

Rabbits show you a short-cut – throw again

Houdini uses magic – go on 2

Slip on a banana skin – miss a turn

up into wis back 1

Arnold's start

Charlie's finish

Hat havoc

"Oh dear, oh dear!" Charlie heard Trader moan, as he passed his store one morning.

"What's the matter?" asked Charlie, hurrying inside. He nearly tripped over a bucket and spade, left right by the door – not to mention a big heap of bananas, another of coconuts, plus shells, pots, pans and lots of other things.

"Oops!" said Charlie. "You can hardly move in here for stuff lying all over the place!"

"I know!" replied Trader. "That's exactly what's wrong! I've run out of boxes to put everything in!"

Trader stepped back and put his foot in a saucepan. CLANG! BONK! CLUNK!

"Gah!" groaned Trader, grumpily.

Charlie hurried off and decided not to return until Trader had calmed down. But he had not gone far when he saw Lewis and Arnold walking along. Suddenly, Arnold tripped and bumped into Lewis, knocking his straw hat off. It rolled away, stopping only when it rested against Edward, who was asleep under a tree.

26

"You clumsy idiot!" snapped Lewis. "You did that on purpose!"

"Er, no I didn't!" replied Arnold. "I'll fetch your hat for you!"

But when Arnold leant forward to pick it up, Edward suddenly began to snore. Startled, Arnold trod on Lewis's hat and squashed it. To make matters worse, Arnold was so surprised he stumbled over Edward and crushed *his* straw hat, too!

"Sorry!" said Arnold, as Edward opened one eye, yawned, and then went back to sleep again.

Lewis picked up both hats. "You can take these along to Trader's store and trade him some beachcombing for new ones!" said Lewis, sternly.

"I wouldn't, if I were you!" called Charlie, hurrying over. "At least, not until he's in a better mood!"

"Well, what do you suggest, Charlie?" asked Lewis. "I mean, I must wear something to keep the hot sun off my head. So must Edward!"

"Easy!" grinned Charlie, getting an idea. "I'll weave you both new hats from big jungle leaves!"

Before long, Charlie had gathered a large pile of leaves. Then he set to work, while Arnold and Lewis sat down in the shade to watch.

"There!" cried Charlie, at last. "I've finished! Try one for size, Lewis!"

Lewis did – and completely disappeared!

"It's huge!" called Lewis. "Get this thing off me!"

"Oo . . . er!" said Charlie. "I've made them both the same size!"

"Thanks anyway, Charlie!" said Arnold. "But I think I'll have to visit Trader's store, after all!"

"Wait a minute. I'll come, too!" said Charlie, who had another idea. He took the two enormous hats with him.

"What can I do for you?" Trader said, almost tripping over some paintings as Charlie and the others arrived.

"I want to trade!" said Charlie. "Listen . . ."

"This hat from Trader's store is splendid. It's even better than my old one!" said Lewis, a little while later. "Well done, Charlie!"

"Yes, rather!" added Arnold. "I won't have to go and do any beachcombing now!"

Charlie felt very pleased with himself as he carried a new straw hat for Edward, too!

Meanwhile, back in Trader's store, everything looked much tidier. Trader had put away all his bits and pieces in the two giant-sized hats that Charlie had made. "They're perfect – just perfect!" he chuckled happily. "That's what I call a good trade. These are even better and bigger than boxes! Clever Charlie! I take my hat off to him!"

28

Trouble at Trader's

The trouble is, there were six things wrong when Charlie and his friends visited Trader's store. For example, Trader is writing with a screwdriver instead of a pen. Can you spot the five other mistakes?

Answers 1 The chair has three legs; 2 Lewis's beak is the wrong shape; 3 The bananas are blue; 4 Arnold's trunk has a knot in it; 5 Trader's moustache is missing.

Taxi!

1 "Where is that taxi?" said Captain Mildred, crossly. "I have been waiting an hour. I have an important meeting with Mary."

2 "Here it is," smiled Lewis. "Sorry I'm late," said Trader. "But the taxi was in a mess, so I had to give it a wash."

3 "Edward! Move over! It's crowded in here," said Captain Mildred. "I wish we had another way of getting about."

4 That gave Lewis an idea. As soon as they arrived at the beach, he started to look for bits of old wood.

5 Soon, Lewis had built his own taxi. "It has more room than Trader's, and it is faster," he told Arnold.

6 Next day, Trader was on his way to pick up Charlie when he spotted Lewis. "I see I have competition," he said.

7 Charlie was a little worried when two taxis raced towards him. "He is my passenger!" shouted Lewis.

8 "No, he's not!" yelled Trader. "Just what is going on here?" cried Captain Mildred, hearing the commotion.

9 "Well, you said we needed a new way of getting about," said Lewis. "Yes, but I didn't mean it!" laughed Mildred.

10 "Trader must have his taxi service!" "But what shall I do with my taxi?" said Lewis. "I know," said Charlie.

11 "Let's chop up the wood and put it on Captain Mildred's fire. Then we can all have toasted scones for tea today!"

Mystery machine

Trader's taxi is not the only way to get around on the island – especially on windy days! Join up the dots to finish this picture, and see how Charlie gets around!

Jungle jigsaw

Charlie's jungle jigsaw is nearly complete. But four pieces have still to be put in place. Which piece goes where? Now name all the animals!

Protect our island

1 Charlie Chalk was out on his usual stroll one morning, when he spotted a black cloud of smoke. "Is that a fire?" he wondered.

2 He rushed to where the smoke was coming from. But he found it was only Trader's old coconut-shelling machine.

3 "The smoke that thing makes is terrible," said Charlie. "It is spoiling the fresh air." "Yes, I know," sighed Trader.

4 "I have ordered a new machine which does not make any smoke," he went on. "Oh, good," said Charlie.

5 A little further on, Charlie had another shock. "The water in that pond has gone all black!" he cried.

6 "It's my new invention," smiled Lewis, proudly. "Do you like it?" "No, I don't," said Charlie. "Stop it at once!"

7 "But it is a great banana-peeler," said Lewis. "You can't spoil the water just to peel bananas," said Charlie.

8 Back at the caravan, Charlie was in a thoughtful mood. "Merrytwit will turn into a rubbish tip if we are not careful."

9 Soon he had an idea. He gave out notes telling everyone to meet him at the caravan. Then he gave out stickers.

10 "Protect our island," read Arnold. "If we don't look after it, then it will not look after us," explained Charlie.

11 And from that day on, Merrytwit was a better place. There was no litter and Lewis even scrapped his invention!

Up to tricks!

Trader was sitting in a rocking-chair outside his store, enjoying the sunshine. Charlie arrived carrying a big, brightly-coloured cushion.

"That's a very smart-looking cushion, Charlie!" said Trader. "It's just what I need. My wooden rocking-chair is a bit hard! I'll trade you for it!"

"It's a special cushion!" replied Charlie, handing it over. "You'd better try it first!"

So Trader put the cushion on the seat of his rocking-chair and sat down. *SQUEAAAAAK!* The loud noise made Trader jump up in surprise.

"Wh . . . What was that?" he yelled.

"My trick squeak cushion!" chuckled Charlie. "I said it was special!"

Later, Charlie saw Lewis and Arnold on the beach.

"Have a look out to sea with my telescope, Lewis!" Charlie called.

"Thank you, Charlie!" said Lewis, holding it up to his eye.

"Hmm! There's nothing to see, except sea!" frowned Lewis.

"Oh, yes there is!" chuckled Arnold, as Lewis removed the telescope.

It had left a black mark around Lewis's eye.

36

"Just an old circus trick!" grinned Charlie. "It washes off easily!"

"Very funny, I *don't* think!" said Lewis.

"I love a good trick!" added Charlie, hurrying off to play more on the other Merrytwit folk.

Later, he was having tea in his caravan when there was a loud knocking on the door. "Charlie! Charlie!" called Lewis. "Come quickly! There's a strange creature out here!"

"What s. . .sort of a creature?" asked Charlie, nervously. Although he didn't say so, he would rather have stayed inside.

"See for yourself," whispered Lewis, as they crept through the jungle. "Look, it's in that long grass! You go first!"

Charlie edged closer. Suddenly, he gasped. A face with two round, white eyes was staring towards him. The creature had a big brown head and long yellow ears. Charlie heard a strange *woo-wooing* sound that made him shiver.

"I've never heard a creature make *that* noise before!" said Charlie. He turned to Lewis. "What do you suppose it is?"

"It's a trick!" replied Lewis, chuckling. "Just like all the ones you've been playing on us today!"

Sure enough, Trader appeared from behind a rock. "I made the noise by blowing through this large shell, Charlie!" he said.

"And that creature is only a painted coconut on a stick, with two bananas for ears!" chuckled Arnold.

Charlie began to laugh, too. "That's the best trick I've ever seen!" he said. But he didn't play another one on the others for a very long time . . .

Merrytwit magic

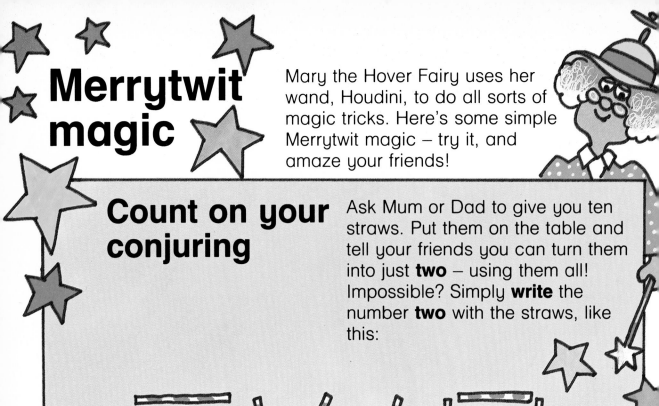

Mary the Hover Fairy uses her wand, Houdini, to do all sorts of magic tricks. Here's some simple Merrytwit magic – try it, and amaze your friends!

Count on your conjuring

Ask Mum or Dad to give you ten straws. Put them on the table and tell your friends you can turn them into just **two** – using them all! Impossible? Simply **write** the number **two** with the straws, like this:

Straight straw

Now say you can bend one straw – but still keep it straight! Your friends won't believe you. Just hold the straw, as in the picture, and quickly move your hand up and down. The straw will look as if it is bending. But when you stop, it will be perfectly straight. Magic!

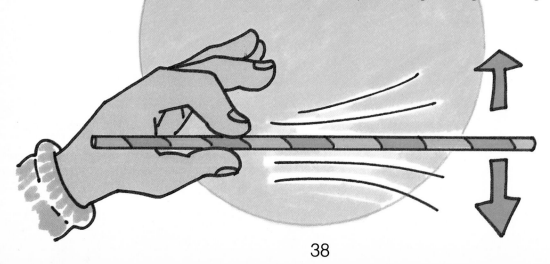

Magic matchbox

Ask Mum or Dad for an **empty** matchbox. Gently tear down the sides at one end to form a flap. Close the flap and the box – and tell your friends it is a 'magic matchbox'. Put in a small coin, like a 2 pence piece. Shake the box so everyone can hear the coin rattle. Then say, "Abracadabra! The coin has disappeared!" Hold the matchbox so the flap is hidden by your hand. Hook it down with your other hand and slip out the coin. Keep the coin hidden. Close the secret flap again. Shake the box – there is no sound. Open it – the coin has **vanished**! Practise this trick first!

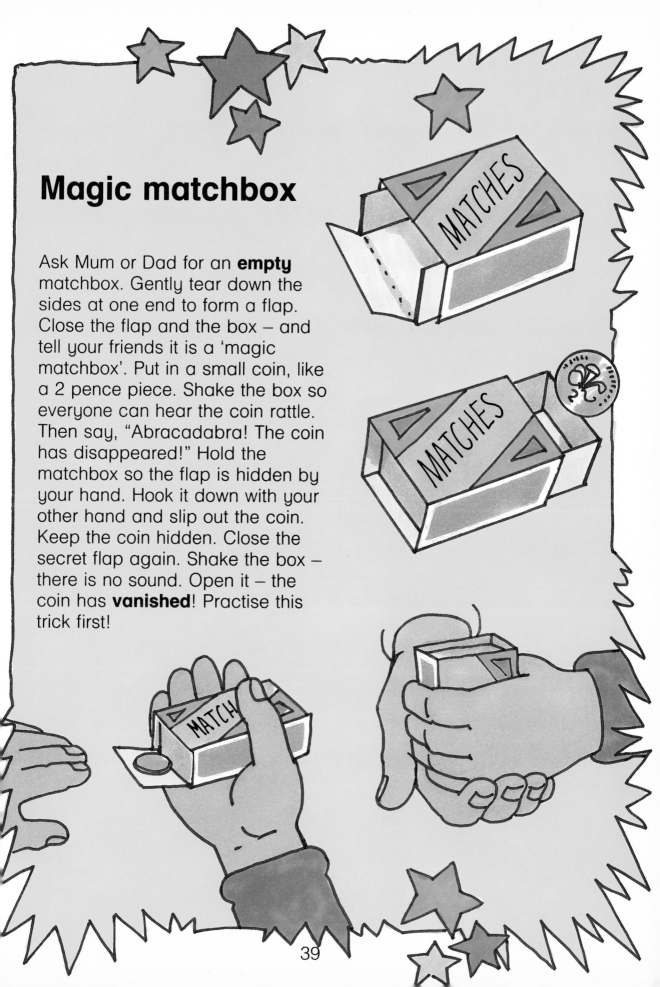

Wash day

1   Charlie Chalk was getting dressed when he spotted Captain Mildred out of the window. She was carrying a big basket.

2   "Where are you going with that?" he asked, rushing after her. "It's wash day, and this is my washing," she said.

3   "Every now and then, the islanders take their washing to the warmest stream," Captain Mildred went on.

4   Charlie hurried home, collected all his washing and followed Mildred to the stream. "Hello, Charlie," said Lewis.

5   The water was lovely and warm, but there was a stain on one of Charlie's jackets. "I can't get this out," he said.

6 "Leave that to me," smiled Arnold. He sucked up some water then blew it at the jacket. The stain was soon gone.

7 "Amazing!" cried Charlie. "Could you blow my washing dry, too?" "No need," said Mildred.

8 She ran Charlie's clothes up the flagpole. "They will dry in the sun," she said. Then Bert arrived.

9 "Am I too early for the ironing?" he asked. "Ironing?" asked Charlie. "What do you mean?" "Watch," said Bert.

10 He picked up Mildred's jacket and pressed it between two rocks. "There is one slight problem," said the Captain.

11 "What?" wondered Charlie, putting on his clean clothes. "Er, sometimes the clothes shrink!" said Mildred.

Muddled message

One evening Lewis and Arnold looked for Charlie on the beach. But all they found was a strange message in the sand. Can you work out what it said?

42

Star performance

"Hey-up and over!" Charlie shouted as he showed Arnold how to do a cartwheel on the beach.

"Bravo, Charlie," said Arnold, clapping. "That's very good. I wish I could be a circus performer!"

"It just takes practice," replied Charlie. "Why don't you have a try now?"

"Well, if you really think so," said Arnold. He took a few paces up the beach. Then he breathed in deeply and ran forward. "Here goes . . .!"

"Good morning, Charlie!" called Lewis, suddenly appearing from a nearby jungle path.

"Oo . . . er! Look out!" cried Charlie. Too late! Arnold spun on to his hands, lost his balance and landed on Lewis before the duck had time to see him. WHUMP!

"S . . . Sorry, Lewis! Are you all right?" said Arnold.

"Of course not! I'm fed up always being bashed and squashed by you!" snapped Lewis, who was very cross. "What were you trying to do, anyway?"

"Perhaps it's safer if you tried juggling, instead," said Charlie, before Arnold could answer. Charlie picked up three coconuts lying on the beach. "Watch me carefully!"

"Hmm! That does look a bit easier," agreed Arnold, when it was his turn.

"Well, I'm not staying here any longer!" said Lewis, hurrying off. "It's not safe!"

"Throw the first coconut into the air, Arnold!" said Charlie.

"Like this?" asked Arnold. But he threw it far too hard. *Whee-thud*! It landed on Lewis's head, making a dent in the middle of his hat.

"Arnold!" yelled Lewis. "Is this yours?" he asked, picking up the coconut.

"Er, I'm afraid it is. You see . . ." began Arnold.

"Don't bother to explain!" replied Lewis. "I've had enough of this. I'm going to Trader's store to get myself a tin hat to wear!"

Charlie and Arnold went, too. "I'll trade some beachcombing hours for it," said Arnold. "It's the least I can do!"

But when they arrived, Trader could not remember where he kept his tin hats, so the others helped him to look for them. As Lewis was busy searching through a big box, under a shelf loaded with paintpots, there was a creaking sound. Charlie noticed it first. He looked up just in time to see the heavily-laden shelf begin to slip at one end.

"Look out, Lewis!" he shouted. But Lewis did not hear, for at that very moment he dropped a metal saucepan, which clattered to the floor.

Arnold rushed forward and took hold of the heavy shelf, just as it was about to fall on Lewis. "H . . . Hurry! Get clear, Lewis!" he puffed. This time, Lewis did not need a second warning. He jumped out of the way and then

they all helped Arnold to lift the shelf down, without dropping a single paintpot.

"Phew! That was rather heavy!" said Arnold, his arms aching.

"I should think so!" said Charlie. "No one else could have held that shelf up all by themselves, like you did, Arnold!"

"I'm sorry I was cross with you earlier, Arnold!" said Lewis. "For once, you *saved* me from being bashed!"

"You'd be perfect in a circus, after all," added Charlie. "As a *strong* man!"

"Er, don't you mean strong *elephant*?" joked Arnold, feeling very pleased with himself.

Pick the path

Arnold went into the jungle to practise juggling with a coconut, a ball and an orange. But he dropped them and they all rolled off in different directions. Can you help Arnold collect them again by picking the correct path to each one?

Answer Path 1 leads to the orange; path 2 leads to the coconut and path 3 leads to the ball.

45

I spy

1 "What a perfect day for sunbathing," said Lewis. "I'll gather the gang right away and we'll go to the beach."

2 "Are you ready yet?" asked Charlie, who had put a towel in a beach bag. But Lewis was dithering in Trader's store.

3 "You have to take sunbathing seriously," he said. "I need sun cream to stop my beak burning, and a cushion."

4 "Then, of course, I need a lilo to lie on, sunglasses to protect my eyes and a book to read . . . oh, and a sunsuit."

5 "Are you ready now?" sighed Arnold, as he watched Lewis try on at least four different hats. He was tired of waiting.

6 Lewis took ages! "Sunbathing is thirsty work. I need a cool drink. I'll just have to squeeze this orange," he said.

7 The others decided to go on ahead. Edward snored, while Charlie and Arnold played I Spy. The time soon passed.

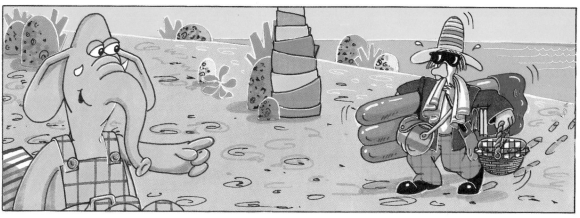

8 "You'll never get this," said Arnold. "I spy with my little eye something beginning with L." Charlie thought hard.

9 "Give up?" laughed Arnold. "It's Lewis, at last." Lewis struggled up the beach with a mountain of gear.

10 "Er, I spy something beginning with C," sighed Charlie. "Lewis, you have taken so long, now it is cloudy!"

11 Poor Lewis! "Never mind," smiled Charlie. "At least Trader will carry everything home in his taxi!"

Charlie Chalk's recipes

Charlie's cheese boats

Charlie enjoys sailing around Merrytwit. But he likes to take some cheese boat snacks with him. Try them for tea.

What you need (to make 4):
2 bridge rolls or French bread pieces
1 small carton of cottage or cream cheese
2 processed cheese slices

What to do:
1. Ask a grown-up to cut the rolls or French bread in half lengthways.
2. Spread some cottage or cream cheese on the bread 'boats'.
3. Ask a grown-up to cut the cheese slices diagonally.
4. Push in cocktail sticks, as in the picture, and push them into your bread 'boats' as sails.

Jungle juice

Charlie's jungle juice is easy to make and delicious to drink!

What you need:
5oz carton pineapple yoghurt
¼pt pineapple juice
1 teaspoon honey

What to do:
1. Pour the yoghurt and pineapple juice into a jug.
2. Add the honey and mix carefully.
3. Pour into one long glass or two smaller ones.
4. For an extra-special treat, top your jungle juice with ice-cream!

Yummy!

A, delicious and B, cooling!

Fruit freezies

Here's a tasty way to keep extra cool on a hot day.

What you need:
5oz carton orange yoghurt
¼pt fresh orange juice

What to do:
1. Pour the yoghurt and orange juice into a jug.
2. Mix together until smooth.
3. Pour into ice-lolly moulds and freeze.

Winning way!

"A, we shall have a **sandcastle competition**!" announced Captain Mildred one morning, from the deck of the Buttercup. "And, B, I will judge it!"

Charlie hurried back to his caravan and fetched his home-made bucket and spade. When he returned to the beach, everyone was waiting to start. "Ready, steady . . . go!" began Mildred, blowing on her ship's whistle. "You all have exactly one hour!"

"My sandcastle will be the biggest!" boasted Lewis, digging in the sand. Beside him, Arnold's sandcastle was taking shape, too.

Even Edward was joining in. "Ho-hum!" he yawned, while he began to dig a moat in the sand. "It's rather sleepy work!"

Mary the Hover Fairy hovered above the sand, working busily. She promised not to use Houdini, her wand, to make a magic castle. "That would be cheating!" warned Captain Mildred.

Charlie kept starting to build a sandcastle, and then knocking it down to begin again. "Hmm! I can't make up my mind what shape it should be!" he said.

50

"I say, everyone!" called Arnold. He looked very pleased with himself. "My sandcastle is nearly finished! And it does look jolly good!"

As he stood back to admire it, he trod on Lewis.

"Ouch! You idiot!" groaned Lewis, hopping about. "Look out!"

Then Lewis hopped on to Charlie's half-finished sandcastle by mistake, and squashed it.

"Oh, sorry, Charlie! That was Arnold's fault! He's such a clown, he should be in a circus!"

"Of course! That's it! Thank you, Lewis!" cried Charlie, beginning to dig in the sand once more. "Now I know just what my sandcastle should look like!"

"Attention, everyone!" called Captain Mildred later. "Time's up!"

She carefully inspected each sandcastle in turn. But when she came to Charlie's, she was very surprised. It was shaped just like a circus Big Top! "They are all very good," said Captain Mildred. "But Charlie wins. His sandcastle is so unusual!"

"It's more like a sand *circus*!" chuckled Charlie.

Look out, Lewis!

"Save me, Charlie!" cried Lewis.
"There's a Duck-eating Snurb by that tree!
It's big and making a horrible noise,
I think it might come and eat me!"

Charlie crept closer, then chuckled,
"It's only Edward, asleep,
He's snoring under some jungle leaves,
Stop hiding, and just take a peep!"

Put these letters in the right order
to find something Edward can
sleep in.

m
o   c
m   a
k   h

52

Store search

Roll up, roll up to Trader's store,
Get everything you're looking for,
Some paint, a jug, a brush and pan –
Try and find them if you can.

A rope, a lamp, a towel, a book,
They're in the picture if you look.
A candle, broom, a pot of glue,
Be sure to search for these things, too!

Put a tick in the circles as you find all the things in the picture.

53

The Bye-Bye Beast

1 "What are you doing?" asked Charlie, when he saw Arnold peering into some bushes. "I have lost Lewis," said Arnold.

2 "What do you mean?" said Charlie. "He must be somewhere." "No, I have looked all over the island," said Arnold.

3 "Well, where did you see him last?" wondered Charlie. "I mean, if he was by the beach, maybe he is still there."

4 Arnold explained that he and Lewis had been searching for the rare Bye-Bye Beast. "We saw a trail by the mountain."

5 "I was checking behind rocks and trees. Lewis was asking Litterbug about the beast, but then he disappeared."

6 "He may have gone into one of the caves," said Charlie. "There are a few by the mountain. Let's go and check."

7 When they arrived at a cave, Arnold said, "How are we going to see in the dark?" Charlie used some magic.

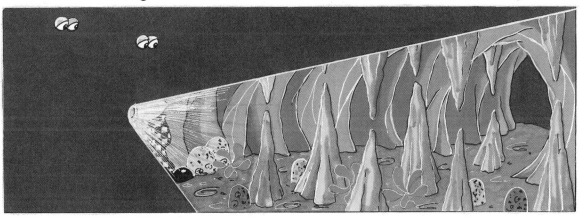

8 He switched on the torch he had just pulled from his hat. Then he felt a tickle. "Stop trying to scare me, Arnold."

9 "I am not doing anything," replied Arnold. "Then who is tickling me?" said Charlie. Suddenly they heard, "Grr!"

10 "Help!" cried Arnold. "A beastly beastie is in here with us!" Both he and Charlie quickly ran out of the cave.

11 And after them came Lewis! "Who growled?" asked Charlie. "I did," said Lewis. "When Arnold stood on my foot!"

Pirate party

Charlie sat on the beach, listening to the sea. He closed his eyes — and suddenly opened them again as he felt a big wave wash over his shoes and trousers.

"That was silly of me," he chuckled. "But they'll soon dry out again in this sunshine."

Meanwhile, Arnold and Lewis had been exploring in the jungle. "All we found was a mud pool!" said Lewis, pointing to his messy clothes.

"It was jolly good fun rolling about in it!" added Arnold, who was covered in mud from trunk to toe.

Just then, Trader came up in his taxi. "Want a lift?" he called. "There's only room for one! I'm loaded up with jungle fruits for my store!"

"You've squashed some on you, Trader!" said Lewis. "See? There are juice stains on your jumper!"

Before Trader could answer, there came the sound of Mildred blowing the Buttercup's whistle. *PHEEEEP!*

"Attention, everyone!" she called, using her loudhailer. "I have something important to say!"

"Better wake up Edward then," said Charlie, spotting him dozing nearby, with sand all over him.

"Huh! Easier said than done!" added Lewis.

But before long, all the Merrytwit folk had gathered by the Buttercup.

"All present and correct, Captain Mildred!" said Charlie.

"And what a sight you are, too!" she said. "Just look at you! It's time you all followed my example and smartened yourselves up!"

"But we don't have uniforms!" said Charlie.

"If you did, you might keep them cleaner than your clothes!" said Captain Mildred. "I think it's time you got some! Over and out!"

"I suppose we could *make* uniforms!" said Charlie to the others, later.

"I'm not sure I have enough material in my store!" added Trader.

"Well, we'll have to think of something!" said Charlie, heading off home to his caravan.

That night, he fell asleep dreaming of himself wearing a special clown's uniform, marching smartly all round the circus ring! But he soon woke as he heard a storm passing over Merrytwit. How the wind howled.

By next morning, though, the sun was shining and the sky was blue. Charlie headed down to the beach. He was still wondering where to get a uniform when he saw something big in the shallows. Charlie could hardly believe it. Neither could Lewis nor Arnold, when he fetched them. For there, washed up by the waves, was an old ship – a galleon.

"It must be hundreds of years old!" said Charlie.

"I bet it belonged to **pirates**!" added Lewis.

"Aren't they supposed to have treasure chests aboard?" asked Arnold.

"Let's find out!" cried Charlie and, before long, they had waded out and climbed aboard.

Water washed around the inside of the ship. Parts of it had rotted away. Arnold slipped and fell on something hard.

"At least he didn't fall on me that time!" said Lewis.

"It's an old sea-chest!" gasped Charlie. "Maybe there is treasure here!"

The catch was rusty and soon broke off. Arnold helped Charlie to lift the heavy lid. But there was no gold inside – just lots of strange, old-fashioned clothes.

"Huh! So much for treasure!" frowned Lewis.

"But these are just as good!" said Charlie.

By the time Captain Mildred arrived to look at the old wreck, all the other Merrytwit folk had put on clothes from the chest. Everyone lined up and saluted proudly. Charlie was wearing a long coat with gold cuffs and silver buttons. He even had a cutlass tied around his waist. Lewis wore big black boots, baggy trousers and a shiny buckle and belt, while Arnold had found a big hat with a feather in it. Edward wore a bright coat – blue, with a purple collar – and he was leaning on a long wooden stick to prop himself up as he dozed.

"Attention, crew – for inspection by Captain Mildred!" said Charlie. "You must admit we all look **very smart** now – just like pirates."

But Captain Mildred shook her head. "A, we don't want **pirates** on this island and B, you all look **worse** than before!" she said. "Take off those old things at once!"

"Can't we wear them just for a while?" asked Charlie.

"Not until tonight!" smiled Captain Mildred. "We shall have a pirate party! Come along. There's lots to do!"

On the beach that evening, under the moon, the Merrytwit folk pretended to be **real** pirates as they enjoyed all sorts of tasty food.

They stayed until the tide turned and the old galleon was washed far out to sea, beneath the waves again.

"We've really enjoyed dressing up!" Charlie told Captain Mildred.

"I intend to dress up again in my best clothes!" said Lewis.

"Rather!" added Arnold.

"I think I will look the smartest from now on!" added Trader.

"Then you won't need uniforms after all!" smiled Captain Mildred. "Charlie, I'd say this party was a **smart** idea, wouldn't you?"

Paper pirate

"Yo-ho-ho and a bottle of pop!" sings Lewis, who likes playing pirates. Why not make him?

1. Trace his head and boots on to a piece of paper. Colour them and cut them out.
2. Fold another piece of paper in half lengthways.
3. Draw lines on it, as in the picture. Ask a grown-up to cut along the lines. Don't cut right to the edge of the paper.
4. Unfold the paper and press out flat. Pull gently at the top and bottom to make a concertina shape.
5. Stick on Pirate Lewis's head and boots!

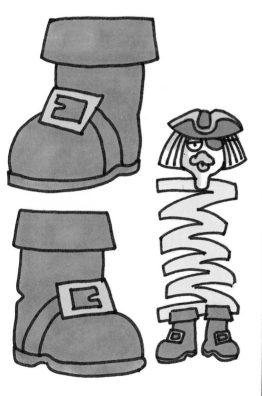

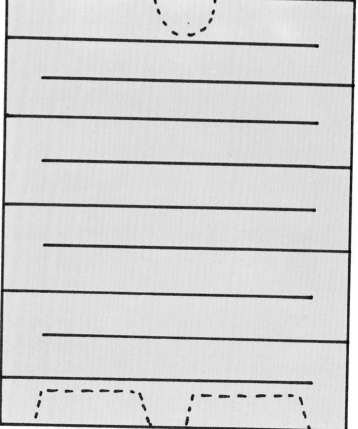

The surprise party

1   It was Captain Mildred's birthday in a few days. "We'll organize a party for her," said Charlie. "And it must be a surprise!"

2   "Who usually organizes the parties?" wondered Arnold. "Captain Mildred does!" sighed Charlie. "I will do it."

3   He went back to his caravan to sort out who would do what. It took a long time, but finally Charlie finished.

4   He read out from his list. "Arnold will make the birthday cake. Trader will wrap all the presents," Charlie announced.

5   "Lewis can make the party hats and streamers and Edward can think of some party games. I think that is everyone."

6 "But what are you going to do, Charlie?" Lewis asked. "Simple," said Charlie. "I will be the party magician!"

7 On Mildred's birthday, everyone stood outside the Buttercup. "Happy birthday!" they called. She was thrilled!

8 "I thought you would forget!" she cried, eating banana jelly. "And what lovely presents you have all brought!"

9 Soon it was time for the games. "Er, well, I did not think of any," sighed Edward. "I had a quick nap and forgot!"

10 Everyone groaned. But then Mildred came up with a great idea. "I know a good game we can play," she said.

11 "Hunt the Litterbug! We can follow his trail of litter, picking it up as we go. First one to find him wins a balloon!"